KU-788-347

LOOK! THERE'S A GHOST

Can you spot them all?

igloobooks

MEET THE GHOSTS!

Time to get spooky! Ten ghosts are hiding on every page in this fun book. Read the profiles below to learn all about their haunting personalities, then look carefully at the scenes to find where each one is hiding. Answers are at the back of the book so you can check your ghost-searching skills!

BOO

KNOWN FOR:
Being the first to boogie at a party

FAVOURITE GADGET:
Headphones

FAVOURITE GAME:
Chase

BLAIR

FAVOURITE SPORT:
Football

FAVOURITE THING TO WEAR:
Football team scarf

LIKES:
Scoring ghouls

SABRINA

MOST-EATEN SNACK:
Cheese on ghost

KNOWN FOR:
Looking fab-oo-lous

LOVES:
Fairground roller-ghosters

CARRIE

KNOWN FOR:
Always being in good spirits

FAVOURITE THING TO WEAR:
Pink bow

MOST-USED PHRASE:
That's spook-tacular!

FRANKIE

FAVOURITE TREAT:
Ice scream

MOST-LOVED ACCESSORY:
Spook-tacles

MOST-USED PHRASE:
Creep it real!

DANA

FAVOURITE FOOD:
Spook-ghetti Bolognese

FAVOURITE THING TO DO:
Haunting people

FAVOURITE COLOUR:
Red

CAIN

KNOWN FOR:
Being really ghoul

FAVOURITE FILMS:
Scary ones

FAVOURITE THING TO DO:
Trick or treat!

THEO

MOST-LOVED ACCESSORY:
Purple neckerchief

FAVOURITE KIND OF SNACK:
Boo-scuits

FAVOURITE THING TO DO:
Ghost walks

BONNIE

BESTIE:
Dana

BEST FEATURE:
Her hair

FAVOURITE BEAUTY PRODUCT:
Scare spray

SAUL

FAVOURITE FRUIT:
Straw-boo-ries

FAVOURITE FILM:
Paddington Scare

FAVOURITE FOOD:
Pumpkin pie

SPOOKY SEARCH

The ghosts love haunting this creepy mansion.
Can you find all ten hiding in this spooky scene?

CAN YOU SPOT THE ONLY PURPLE BAT?

FARMYARD FRIGHTS

Scarecrows aren't the only scary things on this farm!
Can you find where the ten ghosts are hiding?

CAN YOU SPOT THE ONLY PINK OWL?

GALACTIC GHOSTS

Search this space scene to find the hiding places of each of the ten ghosts.

A FUN FAIR SCARE

The ghosts are ready to have a great time at the fair.
Can you find all ten of them among the rides?

ENJOY THE RIDES!

CAN YOU SPOT THE GREEN PUMPKIN?

PEEK-A-BOO!

Ten ghosts have travelled deep into the jungle.
But where are they all hiding?

CAN YOU SPOT THE BLACK CAT?

TRICK OR TREAT?

There are plenty of treats to be found on this page.
Can you find all ten ghosts, too?

CAN YOU SPOT THE ORANGE FROG?

BIG SCREEN SCREAM

Everyone is waiting for the film to start.
Can you find the ten ghosts who are ready to scare?

CAN YOU SPOT THE PURPLE TOFFEE APPLE?

WATER FRIGHT!

Some of the ghosts like to swim! Try to find
all ten ghouls in this busy scene.

COOL GHOULS

The ghost friends love hanging out at the park.
Look very carefully to track down all ten ghosts.

TOY TROUBLE

Not everything in this shop is a toy!
Check everywhere to find the cheeky ghosts.

CAN YOU SPOT THE WITCH'S BROOMSTICK?

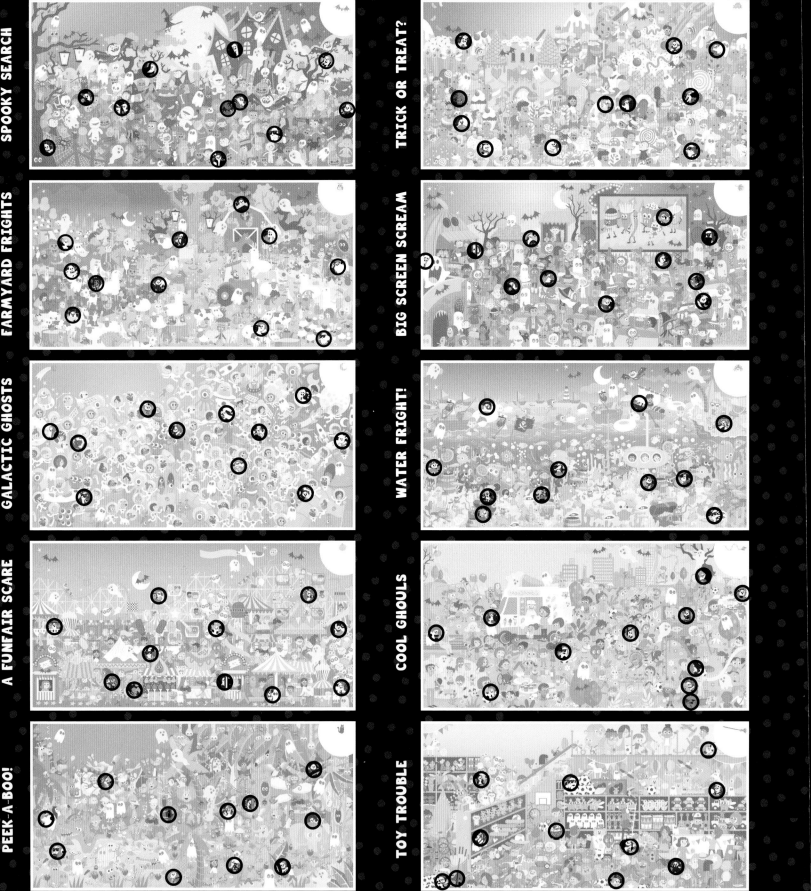

SPOOKY SEARCH

TRICK OR TREAT?

FARMYARD FRIGHTS

BIG SCREEN SCREAM

GALACTIC GHOSTS

WATER FRIGHT!

A FUNFAIR SCARE

COOL GHOULS

PEEK-A-BOO!

TOY TROUBLE